Soaked in love

(A practical guide for new yoga teachers to move from awkward to amazing)

Other titles by Maria Merrill

Being Seen/ Vanity Dare:
How Getting My portrait painted led to new friendships,
understanding, saying yes and sisterhood

I'm not that kind of gal:
love lessons from a hard headed yoga teacher

Soaked in love

(A practical guide for new yoga teachers to move from awkward to amazing)

Maria Merrill

with contributions from
Jessica Boyd, Kathi Crawford, Elaine Eichelberger, Lindsay Parmer, Stacey Ramsower, and Sarah Strom

"The *why* of what we do holds the key to everything that matters. Why we choose the relationships, friendships, trips, collaborations...the *why* brings us back to the beginning. When we go back to our *why* everything becomes simple and clear. Back to the *why* is back to what matters most."

- Sarah Strom

This book is dedicated to those who love to teach, know they are *good*, and are ready to be *great*.

About this book

I use the pronoun "she" to refer to yoga teachers to save space and to recognize that the majority of students who have recently trained to become yoga teachers are women. This pronoun preference is not to imply any disregard for the men who teach and inspire students in their classes.

The format for this book is predominantly questions; questions open up our minds to curiosity and possibility. Getting to know your self profoundly requires diving in. This book is a tool to help you understand your original "why" through peeling away what has clouded your vision or maybe clogged your memory. The questions that make you pause could be the best ones to linger over. Let the answers be revealed to you.

One thing that helps me, before I delve deep into self-reflective work, is to write a "permission slip" to myself, an imaginary sticky note. Taking a moment to ask, "What do I need to give myself that would help me get the most out of this book?"

Maybe it's "to be open minded," "to be kind to myself," "to surprise myself," "to play."

What would you write on your permission slip?

I've asked six friends, yoga teachers I admire and respect, to share their thoughts on what makes a yoga teacher great. Teaching is an art form and hearing from teachers that do it well is inspiring. We all stand on the shoulders of those who have gone before us; we honor the teachers who have shown us the way. We honor the students who are also our teachers.

I changed the title of this book several times, each time thinking I had finally gotten it. I couldn't understand my struggle until I realized I was trying too hard. The answer is simple. To be able to teach yoga is an amazing gift, my desire is to help you become masterful by sharing what I love. This book is *soaked in love* for you.

Disclaimer

You already have everything you need within you. This guidebook can't teach you how to be a better you; what it can do is remind you to shed what is getting in the way. It can remind you to pay attention to your own divinity and those of your students, mentors, and teachers. We are all diamonds in the rough getting polished through our practice.

Become the best teacher of yoga you can be.

Table of Contents

Welcome Dear Yogi,

We each share a love of yoga. We already have that in common. We have been both students and teachers. We have each worked very hard to get where we are on our yogic path. I honor your hard work, dedication and your calling to teach. I honor all the students you have taught and the ones you will teach, I honor the teachers you have had and your future ones, most of all I honor the fact that you wish to grow as a teacher.

I owned a yoga studio in Houston for about a decade; at that time there were not very many yoga studios in town. In the beginning, I taught most of the classes, as the studio grew we needed more teachers and I couldn't find any that I felt were a match. After much self-resistance, I ended up creating a 200-hour training program, and those graduates started teaching at the studio. Over the years teachers from other studios would come practice and ask "Why did our teachers seem different?" "What were they doing differently?" I noticed that many students who were graduating from other programs had a desire for more information and were hungry to become more confident teachers. To fill this need we created a program that took parts of what we did in our training and added things that I felt new teachers in other programs were not getting.

That manual became the basis of this guide. I have added more components for this rendition but the intention from the beginning has been the same,

How to help a good teacher become great.

To be a great teacher is to be the fulcrum on a see-saw. To be able to balance two paradoxical truths. *It's all about you, and simultaneously it has nothing to do with you.* A great teacher straddles those two concepts, and the best way to do this is to get rid of what is not serving. How do you figure this out? Start at the beginning. Some might find this boring, but I disagree.

It can be profound.

As a yogi you already know this, you've experienced this in your own body, any time you literally stack your bones and align your spine correctly you stand powerfully in tadasana. I bet the first time you sensed this you were amazed, how unusual it felt, especially if you had poor posture to start. There is no effort to hold yourself up; your foundation is strong the work is there, but it is not weighty. You have a strong sense of "I've got this." I've got this because it feels right and true in my bones. As tadasana got easier, you felt even more solid. No one can sway you or tell you otherwise because you feel it, you know this truth, and when you are on point, you feel it not just in your bones but in your spirit. You know this so profoundly you can say, "I was born to do this, and I am ready."

Until you aren't.

Some days showing up fully is harder, it feels like work, you are distracted, you had to fight traffic to get to class, or you couldn't find a parking spot, or it's too hot in the room or not hot enough, and now you are at the front of the room, it's time to teach a class, and you feel you've got nothing, *nothing* to give.

"What the hell am I here for?"

"What do I do?"

Or maybe you've been doing a great job but desire a boost. Maybe it is to connect with that thread of yourself that has been woven in and around your teaching but feels about to tear.

There is something wonderfully refreshing about the ability to say, "I'm hungry, I need more." To be able to recognize I don't have all that I need, or to admit what I'm doing isn't working. To ask yourself, "Why isn't this working? It used to work well."

The intention of this guide is to give you what you need and let you travel from "trying" to "being" the teacher you wish to be and are. You will continuously grow as a teacher, but the part of you that can recognize "I am more than enough with what I have at this moment to teach," *that striving gets to rest*. You get to be *you*.

Not very many people are willing to embrace all parts of themselves, the dark as well as the light, especially if there is attachment or belief *that as yoga teachers we are only allowed to be fabulous.* That's a myth, it's exhausting, and it denies half of ourselves. And often it is the student who projects that myth onto the teacher herself. The student needs to understand that her teacher is no different, she's not more of a "rock star" than her. They both are on the yogic path just in different places. This awkwardness at first is not a pretty sight, but if you can say – Yes! That's me. *I am awkward, I can claim that title as one of my hundreds of qualities*, you are already on the path to being a fantastic teacher.

My desire is that this guide gives you what you came for -
And maybe you get not only what you came for but also exactly what you need,

Just like your students do in your class,

I start from the premise that you are already good at what you do, your heart and spirit guide you well, and you are of service to those you serve.

Awkward and amazing here we go!

"If you begin to understand what you are without trying to change it, then what you are undergoes a transformation."

- J. Krishnamurti

Part 1:

Recognize what you already know. Acknowledge your wisdom.

Essential steps to moving forward on your journey include honoring yourself by recognizing where you started and the distance you've traveled to where you are now.

Belief System: Great Yoga Teachers

Anyone who is committed to being a great yoga teacher and sharing what they love about the practice will flourish. We follow those that inspire us, we follow those who believe what we believe, we follow those who share our truth. Each of us has taken a yoga class that we thought was great.

What qualities do you think make a great yoga teacher?

What does a great yoga teacher "feel like"?

What does a great yoga teacher create?

Belief System: Yourself

A belief system is what we know to be true, in answering the following questions be honest and truthful. You have been gifted with wonderful talents that inform your ability to teach, this is not the place to be humble about what you do well. Fill up the page!

What qualities do you have that you know are great?

What qualities do you bring that makes a yoga class great regardless of where you teach?

What do you create for your students?

Belief System: Yourself
Where have your beliefs failed you?

The paradox: just because we believe something to be true does not mean it actually is true. We continuously make up stories and accept them. You might have believed that your 3rd-grade teacher never had fun because she was strict in class and you never saw her smile- then you see her at the grocery store laughing with her husband, and you leave feeling odd- something doesn't compute. Or at your high school reunion, you find out a boy you liked had a crush on you, but you never picked up on it and assumed he was interested in another gal. Each of us has had beliefs that were misaligned.

I used to believe that love was finite. I would very rarely say to anyone, parent, grandparent, family member, boyfriend-girlfriend, "I love you."

because I genuinely believed I only had a finite amount of love to give, so I had to be very choosy who I said those words to and use them as sparingly as possible. I didn't want to run out. Dumb, right? But that was my belief. I didn't know how long I was going to live and how many really important opportunities where I would NEED to say those words, so I rarely said them. Not until my mid-twenties, when I was in my first long-term relationship did a friend call me out, and I questioned my belief. I can't tell you where I got that belief, but it was firmly rooted. Once I realized that scarcity of love was a myth I became more generous and now say those words more often than not.

What's the dumbest thing you have ever believed as an adult?

What happened when you realized that belief was false?

What was the drawback of your belief?

How would that affect your way of teaching yoga? Of being in the world?

How can this knowledge help you develop into a better teacher?

Having looked at your beliefs lets go a little further and look at stories you have made up, both consciously and subconsciously about your students and about yourself. All events, circumstances, or beliefs are neutral until we judge them otherwise. As humans, we are great at judging ourselves harshly. For our own sanity and for the best interests of those we serve. We need to lessen the judgment.

What story have you made up about yourself as a teacher this month?

Was it a "negative" story?

Check in: Is that really true?

One "story" I often fall back into is "I don't know how." I use this as an excuse when I feel overwhelmed or insecure. To fight this tendency, I have to ask myself, "Is it my job to know how? If the answer is yes, How can I learn how? If the answer is no, Can I drop it?" False assumptions can become accidental declarations. i.e. You might believe the story "I need to take care of everyone in my class." Is it true?

Yes, maybe you are responsible for taking care that your students follow your instruction, so they stay physically safe, but are you responsible for their emotional well being? Their spiritual health? If we believe stories without examination, we burden ourselves with things that aren't ours to carry. Stories gain power if we let ourselves hold onto them. Can you drop this story?

Write a positive story about yourself below.

What story did you write? Is it true? If yes, own it! You can't be a strong teacher if you can't see and own your true strengths.

"Are you willing to not recognize yourself
to become who you really are?"

The Four Agreements

The Four Agreements, by Don Miguel Ruiz, is a book we used as the backbone for our teacher training program at Yoga Ananda. The four agreements are: Always do your best, Have integrity with your word, Do not make assumptions, Don't take anything personally. Don Miguel doesn't reference these agreements as being yogic or having a yogic nature, but they are foundational to creating a relationship between teacher and student, and between the teacher and herself.

Why are they applicable here?

How do they serve teachers and students?

What are the benefits of implementing them as a yoga teacher?

What would be some drawbacks if you did the opposite and chose not to follow the Four Agreements as a yoga teacher?

"On this path no effort is wasted,
no gain is ever reversed;
even a little of this practice
will shelter you from great sorrow."

- Bhagavad Gita 2.40

Your Calling

There is an art form to teaching. The what, where, and how of your delivery is essential. The most important element is the "why." The "why" is the window that opens and lets the energy into the room; it's the reason you roll out of your bed happily in the morning to show up at 5:30 am yoga. Your "why" differentiates you from everyone else. Know your "why." Subconsciously or not, your "why" will influence what you share in class, what music you play, or no music, the whole environment you create.

You felt called to share your love of yoga with others, declare your "why" below. Notice the subtleties in the questions and be very specific in your answers. The more specific you are, the more clarity you will have, the more clarity you have, the more certainty you will embody. The person with the most certainty becomes the most effective leader. A powerful yoga teacher leads her students.

What brings you back to your mat?

Why do you practice yoga?

Why do you teach yoga?

Commitment Statement

A commitment is a three-way contract we make with ourselves; our body, our mind, and our spirit. When we choose to commit to something we harness the energy behind our desire. Nothing gets done without desire + committing to action. What are you devoted to? What can you pledge to your yoga practice? What can you commit to for your students? This becomes your mission.

Write your *commitment statement* as a student and teacher.

I commit to

You also have a purpose as a student and as a teacher, your purpose is your "why". You might know this now or it might be revealed to you as you go through this book. What is your mission as a yoga teacher? Why do you deeply desire to teach yoga and serve your students?

Your teaching *purpose statement:*

My purpose is

Truths

You don't need any evidence or proof; you know this in your deepest heart and your gut. Nothing could change these things you know for sure. When you have certainty about a subject, an idea, a truth you act, speak and move through the world with an inner power. This power allows you to step into a leadership role whether you are teaching a class or another aspect of your life, you don't lose it when your class is done, it's part of who you are.

Universal Truths

What do you know for sure? Non-yoga related (i.e self-knowledge is power). List 10.

Yoga Truths

What do you know for sure about yoga from your personal experience? (i.e. we are nothing without our breath.) List 10.

Self Truths

What do you know for sure? About yourself (i.e. I show up for my students.) List 10.

Part 2:

Get out of your own way – remove the "blocks."

Challenges

Every yoga teacher has challenges that come up when teaching. Whether you have a few hundred hours or 10,000 hours of experience you will be tested. These issues will run the gamut; they will be tiny things and giant hurdles. Often in training programs, there is very little time devoted to teaching "real students" not just fellow yogis who already know the poses. Sometimes these challenges might not look like a challenge: your students adore you and your classes. They don't want you to change anything.

All perfect, right?

Right, except you feel like a charlatan, and are horribly bored. Or you have too many students and not enough time slots- a good problem to have but still a challenge to fix.

Challenges give us an opportunity to grow, to stretch so we can make decisions, examine how we want to be in the world, who we wish to become, what kind of teacher we want to be. We get to see what is working and what is not.

I'm not implying that it is easy. It isn't, but there is no such thing as a challenge-free life and your yoga life will reflect your "non-yoga" life. In the struggle to find the best outcome we can become a better teacher, we will definitely become a more experienced one.

What if a challenge is just a question asking to be answered?

How do you want to handle this situation? Do you want to grow or do you wish to shrink?

There is a time for both. Your inner Shiva, your inner warrior, will need to appear- to be firm and clear and not waiver. Your inner compassionate, abundant goddess, your Lakshmi, will also wish to shine. You need both, and you have both to call upon. Usually, a great class is a combination of the two, a balance of sukha and sthira, effort and ease. You can't have one without the other when you are looking for equilibrium.

What are current challenges that you face as a teacher?

Which challenge do you find the most urgent?

What are some quick action steps you could list that would chunk down this challenge into small pieces? List them.

If you need information, you can find it, if you don't know how, you can ask, you have more resources than you realize. Until we get specific on what the "problem " is, it's very difficult to see a solution. Just because you write down the action steps doesn't mean you have to deal with the challenge today -- if it's taking up a lot of mental or emotional space- today might be the perfect day to start taking action. You get to choose.

*"Nothing in the world can purify
As powerfully as wisdom;
Practiced in yoga, you will find
This wisdom within yourself."*

- Bhagavad Gita 4.38

Creating a Safe Space

Students come to yoga for thousands of different reasons. I took my first yoga class because I had incredible anxiety and wanted to get into my body and out of my head. My head was an exhausting place, too many negative thoughts swirling around. It was vital for me to spend time in a space that felt calm and safe so I could learn how to be present instead of living in the past or worrying about the future.

I've had students come to yoga because they are getting a divorce, or they wanted to lose weight to fit into their bridal gown, or they just moved to town and didn't know anyone, or their doctor told them to go, or they want to meet a cute girl or guy, there are so many different reasons and if we don't ask or the student doesn't tell us we have no idea why they show up.

Regardless of why, students need a safe space to practice, and not just a physically safe space but also an energetically safe space. A good teacher can make a student feel safe regardless of where they are, what is going on in the room or who is practicing next to them, or even what is going on in their head. It starts with you.

Getting Grounded

We hold space for our students and ourselves in class. To do this we need to be very present and connected with ourselves and our physical body. We each have specific ways we accomplish this: Breath work, meditation, prayer, chanting, mudras, certain poses or a sequence of poses.

How do you get grounded?

What are the specific practices that you use?

When you're not grounded what have you noticed comes up while teaching?

Class/student "Management"

Whether you teach in a studio, public space, outdoors, indoors, or private lessons you will have issues to resolve. Ideally you create a win/ win situation with your students to make the class work for you too. You might have students who do their own thing and disregard your instruction, students that must have their phone on their mat, must practice in a particular spot, students that bring tons of personal gear into the practice space, students who complain about other students...

What issues are currently coming up?

How can you prepare in advance to handle these situations?

Avoiding the issues will not make them go away. Creating boundaries and guidelines will make it easier for you: saving time and energy that you can direct to doing what you love and helping your students. As humans, we do better when we know what is expected of us. Our brain is calmer when questions we have are answered. If you are new to teaching you might feel the need to please your students and are hesitant to have guidelines in place, get over that hurdle; make it easier for everyone. If you don't like something you can change it!

What can you put in place now to lessen potential hiccups?

Boundaries

Some teachers want to be best friends with their students, some students are very nosey and want to know everything about their teacher. Too many boundaries and the teacher is "armored up" and feels very remote; too loose with boundaries, and the students feel they are not getting a yoga class from their yoga teacher but a therapy or hangout session. Are you placing "your stuff" on your students? Realize what is yours and what isn't. You are not here to solve their problems; you are here to teach yoga. Say "no" when necessary, say "yes" when necessary. Find the middle ground. Stay true to your mission.

*Is there anything you wish to create or dissolve regarding boundaries with
your students?*

Professionalism, Preparedness, Practicalities

Many little things that can interfere with a great class can be solved easily
with foresight. You know by now what kind of arena you feel most
comfortable in- maybe it is a highly structured environment, maybe you
are more spontaneous and like an atmosphere of relaxed mayhem. What
feels most comfortable to you is where you will be able to be your most
authentic self.

*What does professionalism look like for you? What's important to you?
(e.g. being on time; a particular dress code; language, no slang or cursing;
knowing students' names, injuries, physical limitations?)*

*What does preparedness look like for you? (e.g., having a plan for room
set-up, props, class theme, playlist, room temperature?)*

What other practicalities matter to you?

When you have your needs taken care of before you start to teach you can focus on the experience you are delivering.

A Prayer For Recovering Expectation Addicts

"Lord, Shiva, Yahweh, Saraswati, [insert your own deities here], hustle my
shizzle and deliver me to where it's best.
Yess'm, Jesus, Life, cosmic intelligence, Milky Way Magi, take the wheel. I
know you've got my back. I know that you know how intensely my heart
burns, how sweet is the honey at the center of my center, how much I
am capable of. And God knows (that would be you) how game I am to
collaborate with you to make good stuff happen.
I accept my calling: To show up and shine. Unfurled and honest.
Determined to be only that which I am.
I'm here to give my all.
I trust that pure intention counts for plentiful support. I trust we'll get
where I'm going, together.
And I am learning to be where I am.
I'll go make my art now.
I have faith that you've got the rest covered.
The universe will configure around my very best efforts. Willingly. I can
only do what ONLY I can do.
I will do that.
Amen. Om shanti. Shalom."

- Danielle Laporte, *The Desire Map*

Part 3:

Intention and Letting Go

Intention

Intention is the backbone of your class – Putting your intention out there will change people's lives.

What inspires you? What is pushing you? What is pulling you? What do you stand for? What would the people who know you best absolutely know about you and say you stand for?

"Follow the pull.
It's the first step toward flying."

- Danielle LaPorte, *The Desire Map*

Letting Go

Letting go is about service and surrender. Often as yoga teachers, we have to adjust our plans due to who or what shows up in our classes. Sometimes the kindest things we can do for our students is to accommodate their needs and get our ego out of the way. It is our ego that wants to stick with the plan.

- I spent time on my new playlist (!)
- I practiced this sequence before class (!)
- I want to introduce X pose (!)

Any resistance to change is all ego. You can hold onto it or choose to drop it. You might have planned a sequence with quite a few poses. You show up to teach, and the energy in the room is a bit manic, you recognize that the energy needs to ground. You choose longer hold times; you don't get to all the poses you had planned for the class. You go with the flow.

Letting go can also show up as choosing *to not care* if new students like your class. You show up to teach, and eight teenage girls who are new to yoga have chosen your class to fulfill a school assignment. You teach what you've prepared with basic modifications for the newbies. The class is tough for them, and they struggle. Your new students most likely will not return to your class. Did you do anything wrong? No. Maybe your lesson to the teen girls is that yoga takes work, focus and concentration, maybe the lesson was to see how strong their legs are and how weak their back muscles are. Were you a "better" yoga teacher or a "worse" one? Who's to say? What if you were just "being" you? Elevate how you teach.

There are benefits and drawbacks to what you choose, the key element is the intention, what matters to you and why. Whatever happens in class can become a teaching moment for you and your students. You have the power of choice.

Dropping the Plan

When have you dropped a plan for your class before or even during it?

What caused you to do so?

How did that benefit your students?

How did it serve you as a teacher?

Is it easy for you to change plans?

Are you good at practicing nonattachment?

Are you attached to what your class "looks like?"

Do you adjust to circumstances such as your "student population"?

Giving What You Have

This sounds so basic but sometimes we forget. We can only give what we have to give. Some days 10% is all we have to offer.

When have you shown up and not been able to give 100%?

If you were able to only give 10% to that class, how did it benefit your students that day?

Let it be enough. Show up fully. If you only have 10% to give, can you give 100% of that 10%? Students have good bullshit meters. If a teacher is trying to be something she isn't or sharing a yogic lesson that she doesn't believe in, her students will be able to sniff it out immediately.

As a teacher you are perceived as a role model, students will project many ideas, wishes and beliefs on to you. Your task is to find the balance of being true to yourself and faithful to your teachings. It is human nature (the lower self) to run the stories of "I'm not good enough," "I don't know enough," "I'm not flexible enough, strong enough...others are better..." Everyone has these stories depending on who shows up in their class. When you are standing in front of your student you have enough at that moment to teach- you can give what you have to give. Tomorrow you might be able to give more. Any negative self-talk is based on comparison to some other yogi, most likely a fantasy. A belief system of how you think you are *supposed to be.* Who are you comparing yourself to? Comparison is toxic. Drop it. You give what you have to give. It is enough.

How did giving 100% of that 10% serve you?

I love being a guest teacher at a yoga studio or a conference. For me that is amazingly freeing because during that class I can't worry about what any student is thinking of me, I am only there to give them an excellent experience, I probably won't see them again. If they don't like the class that is okay. I deliver what I can.

I love not knowing anything about the students before I teach, there are no identities to get in the way. One of my students brought her mother to class one time, and her mother was a pretty well known movie actress, "a movie star." I didn't give her mom a good experience that Saturday morning because I was very intimidated by her. I was so invested in her getting a *good experience* that I gave her very little of *any* experience. I wasn't present with her. I paid attention to the other students in the room but gave very little attention to her. I thought she was "used to" great yoga teachers – she lived in California (!) How could I live up to that? I gave up before trying. I was a new teacher and very concerned with wanting to please. If I hadn't recognized her, I would have treated her just the same as the others, and I would have stayed present and authentic. The ego gets in our way. Let go of comparison.

"Fools say that knowledge and yoga
are separate, but the wise do not.
When you practice one of them deeply,
You gain the rewards of both."

- Bhagavad Gita 5.40

Part 4:

Authenticity and Connection

Vulnerability vs. "The Yoga Teacher Mask"

To be vulnerable is to be unguarded, it takes courage to allow ourselves to be seen and "exposed" even when it is by choice. When we choose to show our vulnerability, we are demonstrating that we care enough about something to be willing to put ourselves at "risk." The "risk" might be rejection, misunderstanding, or lack of connection. We share a personal story, or let the students know we are nervous or having a hard day maybe not in words but through our voice cracking or our shift in energy. Each of us has had moments when a friend or teacher has shown vulnerability. It is in that precise moment that we become aware of her vulnerability and recognize that she is the bravest one in the room.

We honor that courage-even when we might not agree with it. When you show up honestly, therefore courageously, no one can find fault with you as a teacher. One of the most honest and vulnerable answers to a student's question is to answer "I don't know." The mastery comes in balancing your knowledge with your lack of knowledge. Your students still want a leader. They want it to be you.

Vulnerability

When or how have you shown vulnerability as a teacher?

What happens if you don't show your "humanness"?

What happens if you show too much?

"Yoga Teacher Mask"

As a new teacher, you might have quite a few preconceived ideas of what you are *supposed to* sound like, how you *should* behave, how many "followers" you need on social media to be considered *good.* In trying to be who you are not, you exhaust yourself, feel like a sham, use all your energy to pretend or prove something, you burn out.

Sometimes this desire to be a certain way – comes from trying to "protect" or "shelter" your students or to sell the lifestyle you love- a daily yoga practice, a weekly practice, whatever it might be, and it unintentionally exaggerates the problem.

Once I had a student tell me after class "You are so lucky – you are surrounded by yoga every day, you probably don't get angry, you don't have any stress." I wanted to shout at her, "You have no idea!" I didn't yell, but I sure wanted to.

The myth of the perfect yoga teacher is large in our western culture, and the stereotype has changed over time. It used to mean hippie-dippy-flighty-not-smart-in-business-vegan. If TV commercials are to be believed, now the myth is a size two, super flexible, 20-year old beauty with a stress-free life. This "yoga teacher mask" contributes to the challenge of being an authentic teacher. There are powerful yoga teachers who are in their 20's are a size 2 and are beautiful, there are hippie-dippy-yoga teachers that are extraordinary and then everything in between.

What about you? Have you worn a "yoga teacher mask" while teaching? If yes, what is it? And why? What shows up?

"Let yourself be silently drawn
by the stronger pull of what you really love.
Your task is not to seek for love,
but merely to seek and find all the barriers
within yourself that you have built against it."

- Rumi

Authenticity
Finding your voice/ Taking your seat

Authenticity originated from the Greek word Athentikos- one who does
things himself, genuine, undisputed origin, real, true.

What does authenticity mean to you?

What has it cost you and your students when you don't practice it?

What happens when you don't allow yourself to be authentic?

I'm not advocating sharing everything when you teach, let me be very
clear. In my experience teaching works better when there are a few
boundaries. I'm advocating authenticity in what you *select to share.* You
can be authentic and choosy. There are many yoga teachers that share so
much there is little space for yoga practice.

There is a time and place for each – the mastery of teaching is knowing
when and what to share and what depth of authenticity is best for your
students. You can share you had a rough day and weave that into your
teachings. This makes your teaching universal instead of personal. Your
belief in what you are sharing will let the energy flow and connect with

them. For that rough day in class, don't share that you have a headache
and you wish you were not in class and would rather be home on the sofa,
they don't need to know that- that doesn't help. Tell them about doing
what you need to do even when it is challenging
- they came to you for yoga. Give them yoga.

What's the benefit to your students of being authentic?

What's the benefit to you?

What do you feel comfortable sharing?

When/how have you been authentic as a teacher?

What does authenticity look like to you?

Authenticity can be energizing, efficient and economical. Authenticity builds trust, courage and your comfort level. Authenticity is a practice. Yoga is a practice. The best gift you can give your students is yourself. Let yourself spread out into your true self, let yourself expand instead of trying to contain yourself in a box, whether it is teaching a yoga class, having dinner with your friends or just being in this world. The more we are genuinely ourselves- not trying to be something we aren't, we become the best version of us possible. Authenticity is why students come back to your class, that is why you have the friends you have, they resonate with you and vice versa. That doesn't mean they will love everything you do all the time. You give them something that satisfies something they seek.

Don't take it personally when students *don't show up or when they do*, it might be the time slot, the place you teach, the convenience of the studio class, but that is only at the beginning. If they like your class they will follow you to another location, another time slot, they will follow you when you change your style of teaching, when you add music, when you take it away, until they decide they don't want to take your class anymore. It might be the new location, the time slot, the traffic, it might not have anything to do with you. It might be because of you. They've changed, and you've changed, and that is perfectly normal.

Nonattachment makes us more authentic and more effective as teachers. We stop trying to be who we are not, we recognize that we are enough, all that we need is already available.

Connection to others and ourselves happens when we are willing to "show up" at a deeper level, "flaws" and all, and that makes us human. If you can take it in stride when you demonstrate a pose and lose your balance don't worry about the fact, don't blush, it's not a big deal. Sometimes you repeat a pose or do one side twice remember it's not the end of the world.

Many new teachers are not yet comfortable being fully "seen." Instead we show up as various parts of "fantasy" selves, the yoga teachers that mentored us, that fabulous person in teacher training, the yoga teacher who always has a full class. All that work of trying to be someone you are not takes you further from the truth.

*"Don't be satisfied with stories,
how things have gone for others.
Unfold your own myth..."*

- Rumi

Finding your Voice

It is not about you -- it is all about you, and your students come first. We are starved for "the "real", we want to "feel" the other person, they want to connect with us, your students want to connect to what is real within *themselves*. Give yoga time to do its work.

Why does your voice matter? (Write for 2 minutes uninterrupted.)

Pay attention to what pulls your attention. What interests you and draws you in is going to make your class "yours."

Magic happens here.

What do you pay attention to? (Write for two minutes uninterrupted.)

How could you use what you just wrote in your teaching?

Taking your seat

"Asana" at its origins means to take your seat. To be a teacher, to be a contributor here in the world you need to claim your seat; you are being asked to do that now. One way to do this is to be clear, *who do I want to be as a teacher?*

I am a quitter. I quit the things that do not serve me.
What is not serving you?

I heal what needs healing.
What needs healing?

I choose to stop apologizing.
What have you been apologizing for? Can you choose to stop?

Playing Big -- Showing Spunk

Where in your life have you dared greatly? What happened?

When to risk and when to hold back is a big question. You learn by listening, by trusting your intuition, by the clarity of your intention to the class. Hesitation vs. intuition vs. fear this is the balancing act.

Will what you share add value or detract?

Who is the information for?

Have you said too much?

Where in your life have you demonstrated courage over fear?

You have done so thousands of times over your life. Maybe it hasn't shown up as much in yoga, but I bet it has. Maybe it was when you showed up for your first yoga class and you walked through the door due to curiosity. It can be that simple.

When are you fearless?

Connection

Where and when do you feel it?

How does it feel in your body? What sensations does it bring up?

What does connection do for your class and your students?

Is there anything you need to be able to be, do, or have so that you can connect deeper?

Sometimes daily life gets in the way and we get separated from what we love; we disconnect from ourselves. Sometimes the best thing we can do is give ourselves a moment to hit the pause button. To take a breather and reflect, *what have I given up on? I really love that. How do I give that back to myself?*

I have found that teachers-to-be, and even seasoned teachers, have often given up on certain ideas of who they believe they can be. Or what they believe they can have for themselves because they have chosen "yoga." You don't have to be altruistic and never charge for your services just because you teach yoga. Pay yourself well if that is important to you. Just because you are great at teaching restorative classes doesn't mean that you have to give up on learning to be a "kick ass" yinyasa teacher. Give yourself permission to be the teacher you wish to be. Give yourself permission to be the person you wish to be.

Have you given up on who you can become as a teacher? If yes, what have you given up on? (Write for 2 minutes uninterrupted.)

Is there anything you need that you are finding hard to get?

Give yourself that which you are seeking. Your connection to yourself grows deeper when you can trust yourself to nourish and take care of your own needs, whether spiritual, financial, physical, vocational etc.

Clarity

Having clarity gives you certainty and direction. It focuses your energy, so you can create with ease.

What are you grateful for in this moment regarding yourself?

Create moments for gratitude to come in.

What do you hold sacred?

"We are what our deep, driving desire is.
As our deep, driving desire is,
So is our will.
As our will is, so is our deed.
As our deed is so is our destiny."

- Brihadaranyaka Upanishad IV 4.5

Part 5:

Judgment, the "F" Word, and Success

Judgment

You want others to judge you.

Yes, that statement is true and it is a good thing. We judge things all the time. It keeps us safe or efficient. It keeps us in our comfort zone or pushes us out of it.

We smell food that has been in the fridge for several days, forgotten leftovers. "Is this still okay to eat?" We sniff and toss it into the trash or consume. Is it best to get on the freeway at rush hour or take the back roads? What is going to be most efficient time-wise? You test and learn- that route saved me time, that second choice did the opposite. Yoga students do the same.

The only way your students will know if you are a match for them is if you are true to yourself, and give them the opportunity to judge your teaching. They will know quickly. You might be tolerable to them- (ouch!) the class time is good, they will stick around, they like you but not the parking situation or the subway route, they don't return. Many factors come into play whether students choose to return or not but more than anything else it starts with you. Ideally, you will have students in a class that resonate with you.

Train your mind to embrace judgment. Like friendships, you get to decide. Do you want ten students that show up again and again and grow and develop their practice? Do you want 85 in a class and to be the "rock star" yogi who has followers and fans? One is not better than another, either way, you will experience pleasure and pain as a teacher and unique challenges. Students are seeking their teacher. Let your tribe find you. The perfect student that needs to hear, see, and experience you as their leader.

Judgment doesn't stop at the class door but shows up with your co-workers and your "boss." This is good too.

How does it feel to embrace the concept of being judged as a yoga teacher?

Can you embrace it?

The "F" Word
FEAR

New teachers, and even seasoned teachers, have fears that surface. Fears that come up when faced with a large class, or a small class or a class of beginner students. This is the human condition. Having fears when we face something new, being uncomfortable doing something different is normal, like judgment, can you embrace it or ignore it? Neither will stop them from occurring. Fear is a sensation we will never be able to get rid of completely. it does serve us. Figure out how to harness it for your own good.

Some common yoga fears:

I'm afraid I will screw up.
I'm not as confident as other teachers; I'm afraid my lack of confidence will show.
I'm afraid I don't know enough to teach a yoga class well.
I'm afraid that the students won't like me or my class or my style.
I'm afraid that I won't be "good enough" as a teacher.
I'm afraid it will be hard to compete as a yoga teacher with so many qualified teachers.
I'm afraid it will be difficult to find a place to teach.
I'm afraid that if I "mess up teaching" I will be judged.
I'm afraid my body will be judged -- I don't look like what a yoga teacher is "supposed to" look like.
I'm afraid I'm too old compared to other teachers.
I'm afraid I'm too young, students won't listen to my life experience.
I'm afraid I have less to give my students than other teachers.
I'm afraid of handling difficult students in a class.
I'm afraid of not knowing how to "deal with" students with specific health issues.
I'm afraid I won't know how to teach a really_____ (pregnant, obese, elderly) student.
I'm afraid I will have students that are better at yoga than I am.
I'm afraid a student will get injured in class.
I'm afraid of really being seen.
I'm afraid my students will leave me if I make changes in my class.
I'm afraid if I teach more there will be no time for me to practice.
I'm afraid students will notice I am _____, (bored, a fake, inconsistent, nervous)
I'm afraid I have plateaued as a teacher, and I won't grow.
I'm afraid this is a big mistake, I can't do this.
I'm afraid of not having the answer to a student's questions.
I'm afraid I won't be as popular as another teacher.
I believe teaching is easier for others than for me.

How did it feel to read this list? What did you notice?

Could you relate to any of the fears listed above?

List some of your own fears.

How does it feel to know that these are universal fears? If you traded out just a few words, this could be a list of fears anyone might have going to a first date, a job interview, or asking for a raise. You are not alone, it is uncomfortable to put yourself out there. The above list is taken from students in our past teacher training programs. These are real fears. Let me repeat. You are not alone. Whatever you are feeling is valid. If a fear of yours is not listed doesn't mean it's not normal. Let that sink in.

Marianne Williamson has a great quote in "A Return to Love" where she pushes back against all the self-talk we have *about not being good enough*. Or *I don't know enough*. I hear myself say these things even today, and I'm tired of it, it's such an old story, for me, those fears come up now, not when I teach yoga, or at least not very often when I teach yoga, they now come up with writing. In organizing this book for you to read, "who do you think you are?" is my enemy. "What do you think you, Maria, can offer that hasn't already been said about teaching yoga or becoming a better teacher?" I respond to this small persistent voice, and I'm paraphrasing here, with Marianne's response, "Who am I not to be?"

That answering question makes me smile and grounds me. Indeed, "Why not me?
Why can't I write and share what I have learned about teaching yoga over the years? Yeah!
Why not me?
Why not you?"

That's the whole point of this guide, for you to do what you were born to do, what you feel called to do.

I was flipping through TV stations the other week looking for a program, and I paused for a moment to watch *The Voice*. If you are not familiar with it, it's a singing contest that pairs singers with coaches as mentors and TV viewers get to pick the winner. What I noticed in those ten minutes is that most of the performers were singing songs that had been recorded by other artists. It didn't matter that the songs had been sung by someone else before, the contestants were giving the songs their *own voice*.

It's so simple and yet we forget.

It's the same with teaching a yoga class or baking a cake or any other form of creative expression. No one else can do it as you can so you better hurry up and share what you want with us because we want to see it, or hear it, or experience *what only you can deliver*. Imagine how boring it would be if there were just one person able to teach a class, only one type of chocolate cake and only one person to bake it, one type of book and only one author. How many thousands of songs have been written about love? How many poems have been composed? How many wonderful teachers have you had the joy to study with?
Who cares if the topic you are sharing in yoga has been shared before? No one can teach precisely like you.

No one.

Fears will show up. Again. You will conquer them and they will return in a slightly nuanced new version. You will again conquer them. It's a dance. What you are feeling is valid. What you feel might be common or uncommon, rational or irrational. It is still yours. You get to choose what to do with it.

There is this interesting thing in yoga that stalls us. Yoga is about union and many studios, and teachers strive for community, I know I did and still do as a teacher- but so many teachers, especially new teachers, feel alone regardless. They feel they can't exhibit certain qualities because they will lose their students or not get any in the first place, or won't be respected or don't want to appear ignorant. This isn't unique to you if you fall into this category. It is not just teachers but studio owners too. Studios are businesses, and the business needs to stay open. Fears of scarcity or competition can surface. We can go down those rabbit holes if we are not careful.

I'm super tired of the Gandhi quote "Be The Change You Wish To See In The World"- YES. But enough already, his words are brilliant, however every email from a yoga studio or an Instagram post recently seems to say this routinely. It begins to feel inauthentic depending on who says it. Sometimes we spout stuff but don't have the energy *to walk the walk*. I know I have been there, not that I like to admit it. It's lazy. We are fearful of going deeper, of truly being seen. Rephrase the question, instead of repeating what someone else says ask "what quote represents me doing the work?" Find the quote that truly represents you and your teaching. Stay out of the lazy lane.

Teach.

To become masterful conventional wisdom says you have to practice your skill 10,000 times.

How many times have you taught?

Exactly.

Can you let up on your own expectations and just show up?

His Holiness the Dali Lama often quotes the Buddhist belief, "All suffering comes from attachment," Let go of the attachment and you let go of your stress around your fears. Your first class might suck, your 500th class might bomb. So what? You're human, fabulous, so is everyone else in your class. You fell in love with a practice, remember teaching is a practice.

I'm not making light of your fears here. I am sharing that they are universal. There are many baby steps you can do to help yourself. My advice? Get curious. Stay curious.

I was terrified, as a new yoga teacher, of having a second or third-trimester pregnant student in my yoga class. I hadn't experienced pregnancy; I didn't know what that felt like, how could I relate as a teacher? My first yoga training barely touched on the topic, and of course, I attracted that exact student to my class, and it went okay, not great, but okay. I read books, I went to special workshops, I took a prenatal yoga class, I asked questions, I got curious. I gained knowledge and experience. I learned I didn't have to know it all, I could ask my pregnant student questions, it was okay not to know. My fear began to subside. You will do the same- and certain fears after a few more hours teaching won't even be concerns. You will get new ones to replace the old ones, and you will realize, fear will be there, but it doesn't need to interfere with you being a fantastic teacher. Failure isn't an option, it's reality, and it's okay to flop, you can mitigate it, and it would be wise to have a contingency plan.

Part 6:

Wisdom

What makes a yoga teacher great?

This question was offered up during a five-day yoga retreat many years ago when I had been consistently teaching for about a year. The teacher didn't give any handouts or absolutes on the "correct" answer. The afternoon conversation struck me profoundly because there were so many different views on what that might be. I have asked that same question at our Yoga Ananda teacher trainings and loved the conversations that ensued. When I graduated from my first 200 hour teacher training I had a wonderful yoga mentor, she was the owner of the first studio where I taught; I also wished that I had heard from other teachers. Many of the books I read were written by "famous" male teachers, lovely and helpful as they were I wanted to hear from those that I could relate to easily.

The six yogis below generously answered my call and contributed the "advice" below. These wise women inspire me as a student and as a teacher. Similar to Rainer Maria Rilke's "Letters to a Young Poet" let yourself be with where you find yourself, there is no "have to" that you must complete or change to be a better teacher due to what is written below. Take with you what resonates. These essays are given with love, and all come from a place of personal experience.

The writings are listed in the order I received them. I liked the way the themes overlap and ripple out, different voices, same desire to be of service, to share personal wisdom. I felt I was unwrapping little gems in my email box as they popped up, and I usually don't look forward to checking emails, this was different. These are a delight.

What makes a great teacher?

You learn how to be a great teacher by teaching. There is really no way around it. You have to teach for a while to learn the rhythm of the room, the students, and the pace of the class. A great teacher is comfortable in her own skin and teaches what she knows to be true to her, both spiritually and through her own body and personal practice, and she shares that with her students. She speaks from a place of giving and service.

A great teacher is someone who is authentically herself, and her inner light shines through. She connects with her students in a real way and yet holds space for them to grow and transform. Yoga is a practice that requires strength, focus, growth, transformation, dedication, and letting go. The teacher helps the student be ok with where she is on her journey.

Each teacher has her own unique message to share, a message that needs to be shared that only she can give. The messages I've received from my favorite teachers have come when they shared with me exactly what was needed to come through them; not what they thought they needed to share or what a class theme needed to be, but real life, day-to-day truth.

Teaching a great class takes time, energy and effort. A great teacher puts forth the effort to plan a class. She dedicates time and energy to continual growth and learning and has a yoga practice of her own. The times when I have been burnt out from teaching, or feeling inauthentic doing it, were when I wasn't practicing and was teaching too many classes. I believe now that self-care is a major component of a good teacher. You have to have your cup full to give and serve others. If you are giving from a dry cup, both you and the students can feel it. The teachings will fall flat.

Lindsay Parmer is a mother of 2 boys, wife, yoga teacher, preschool teacher, lover of 70s music, meditation and essential oils. When she's not doing something with her boys, she is exploring some dimension of creativity, spirituality or healing.

When I think of the qualities of a yoga teacher that makes me want to return to his or her class, I think of a "package deal" – a class that incorporates all of the components of an ancient yoga practice: mind, body and spirit connectedness. Yoga teachers that draw me deeper into my practice and have me wanting more frame an asana practice around mindfulness and breath integration. By beginning with an intention that stems from a classic yogic concept or mantra or even a contemporary quote, and returning to that intention throughout the practice, allows me to be intentional and focused. When my mind wanders and is brought back into my body through steady breathing and thematic instruction, my physical practice becomes truly a moving meditation. Only a yoga teacher that has a strong practice of their own can help make this happen for me.

My initial experience with yoga was limited to Bikram yoga, where the teacher recites a memorized dialogue that Bikram himself wrote, during each and every class. No variation. No spiritual connection with the ultimate purpose of yoga. Yes, there was breathing and mindfulness preached, but it was not integrated in any meaningful way. It felt like simply a physical practice with only the inflection of the teacher's voice to personalize their teaching method. For many years, that's what I thought teaching yoga was all about – and as long as I did not get criticized or called out, I was good with this type of practice. It was only when I branched out and found other forms of yoga, that I began to realize what teaching yoga – and teaching yoga well actually meant.

I now understand what makes a great yoga teacher: the combined ability to gain inspiration from one's own mind, body and spirit connectedness, and then to transform that inspiration into a yoga class and yoga sequence that takes students on a journey allowing the students to find their own connection within themselves. It takes a lot of work, a lot of hard work, first with a personal practice, and then with the amount of time needed to prepare a class that tightly weaves the fruits of that connectedness into a message that will resonate with students. Every day is different, and there is no prescribed formula for every class, but meditating on something that resonates within oneself can inspire the most meaningful experiences for both yoga teachers and students.

Elaine Eichelberger is a devoted yogi, yoga teacher, writer, wife, mother, enthusiastic cook, lover of all sweet dogs and Dean of Students at St. Agnes. When she is not teaching she enjoys cooking for friends and family.

Remember the Why.

Whether you have been teaching for six months or six years, there will be times when you will "be hard" on yourself. Maybe you said left when you meant right; maybe you forgot what comes next in your sequence; maybe you have a week or even a month when you just feel "off." Needless to say, there are probably going to be times when you want to quit. When you feel like you're just not doing enough as a teacher, and as a person. When this feeling comes, because it probably will, please remember that you're not alone. We've all been there. Heck, some of us might be there right now. Especially in these days with Instagram and Facebook telling us that we need to be doing more-- more self-promotion, more photos in forearm stand, better music in class, more complicated sequences-- you name it, and pretty soon, all of the yoga that you know in your heart to be true is gone.

I've been teaching for almost six years, and I remember the first class I taught like it was yesterday. I also remember when my teacher came to visit my new studio after about six months of it being open. I was nervous. She was in class and just as she had always done, she took notes on critiques. After class, she handed me her notes. Upon looking at them, I began to cry. I walked outside of the studio and thought to myself, "What the heck am I doing?" "Who do I think I am?" Cue the critics that Brené Brown refers to. I was slumped over by the side of the street. The tears poured down my face as I berated myself about every little thing I should have done differently. I let myself cry. I let myself feel bad. This was actually really familiar to me. This feeling captured exactly what I did to myself if I fumbled over my words or made any little error in class. I was hard on myself, really hard on myself. After about 20 minutes of crying and feeling in complete despair, something shifted in me. I thought to myself, I can either let this define me or not. I began to remember back to my first classes as a student. I thought back to what my time on my mat has taught me so far. I thought back to hearing my teacher's words wash over me, which encompassed the very heart of remembering why we take the risk, to put ourselves out there, and show up to teach day after day, it's not about us.

Teaching is not about us. It has nothing to do with our sequences, but it does have everything to do with getting ourselves and all the things we place on ourselves out of the way long enough to hold space for our students. The day that my teacher came to the studio, I wasn't teaching from my why. I was trying to show her that I was a "good teacher." I wasn't in my true *why*, I was in my ego. You see, the minute we go into our self-criticism or self-doubt is the moment we lose our "why" and the ego takes over. Suddenly, we start trying to force words out of our mouths and become an awkward mix of the teacher we think we should be and the teacher we really are. It becomes about us, about what we are presenting. The actual yoga, the heart of what we are trying to give, gets lost.

The best thing that I can offer here at this moment is to say that no matter where you are in your teaching; no matter if you are brand new, haven't even taught your first class yet; or you've been teaching for years, just remember your why. Remember your why, and it will always bring you back to your roots and back to yourself. Your why will give you strength and remind you to keep going. Come back to it. Come back to it over and over and over again.

Sarah Strom is a writer, yoga teacher, backpacker, skier, and student. She is an Integrative Institute Holistic Nutrition Advisor, Embody Love Movement Facilitator, as well as Owner & Founder of The Yoga Collective at Maitri Yoga, LLC.

"Dear one" is how one of my teachers, Judith Hanson-Lasater, always addresses her students in written communications. This informal, endearing address makes me feel welcome into her space and ready to receive her heartfelt insights and wisdom. I wish to extend this address to you, dear one, as I share a few nuggets of what I have learned as a yoga teacher and practitioner and as a human being.

I came to yoga to improve my performance on my bike. Prior to cycling, I was an avid runner. Unfortunately, when training for my first marathon, I experienced a hip injury I learned, at that time, about alignment (or in this case, being out of alignment). Being hunched over on a bike for long-distance rides started to take a toll on me. I was working out with a trainer who recommended yoga and started attending class at the gym. What my teacher opened up for me is that yoga asana practice was a gateway to learning about myself and to engage in inquiry around my practice and my life.

One day I was sitting in the chair chatting with my hairdresser, and we started to talk about yoga. He recommended his favorite yoga studio. At Yoga Ananda, I began a deeper journey into my yoga practice and eventually signed up for teacher training. My intention for completing the training was to deepen my practice. I did not plan to teach! After all, I had a successful career and business. It was at some point during the training that I realized I was being given the gift of teaching so that I could give the gift of yoga to others. I sought to find a way to bring what I was learning in my yoga practice and in teaching yoga to the workplace. Since then I have designed a program for teams in companies that teach basic principles of yoga and inquiry. And, I have been teaching yoga!

Following are the nuggets I would like to share with you. My hope is that what you are learning in this book inspires and encourages you to share yourself as a teacher and practitioner of yoga in whatever form and method that speaks to you.

Nugget #1 – Develop and Nurture a Home Practice

The Sanskrit word Svādhyāya is simply "to study one's own self" and is one of the three key elements in the practice of yoga defined in the Yoga Sutras of Patanjali. Given my occupational background, the study of human behavior has long been a part of who I am, not only with my personal journey but also in the context of how people behave in organizations. Understanding Svādhyāya, however, goes beyond the behaviors and motivations one may have. This self-study practice also challenges us to contemplate our circumstances and the environment we are in and to assess where we are in our life, what is our life direction and how certain changes may lead to a more fulfilling life.

I have found that developing and cultivating a home practice allows for deeper introspection to happen. Interestingly, it took quite some time for me to create what I consider a meaningful home practice. The first issue was finding the space in our townhouse for my practice as every space was essentially taken. Eventually, I found sitting in front of the fireplace for meditation and journaling worked for me, but I continued to take my asana practice at a studio. It is only in the past few years that I have been able to carve out a room in my house for my home practice, and I can teach private yoga classes in this space. And, the truth is, space does not have to be carved out. Many a practitioner and teacher have practiced yoga asana in a hallway or in the kitchen or anywhere they could place their mat, "on the mat" is where the practice is.

Another key to creating a Svādhyāya practice is to create a routine around it and just do it! Build it around what inspires you or what you are curious about. One ritual I enjoy is to choose a book that I wish to read or that has meaning for me and read a passage each day. For example, I have been reading "Meditations from the Mat: Daily Reflections on the Path of Yoga" by Rolf Gates. I will set my meditation timer to include the time I read this book. Once I feel I have read enough, I will meditate. If inspired, I will journal what I learned from the passage and reflection. And, if the passage felt shareable, I will write it down in my journal or tag the page so that I can share in my teaching. It might be an idea or topic to set the intention for a class that I want to build upon.

Finally, I believe it is important to be gracious with yourself in this process. It is not a "goal" or a "have to" wherein if it doesn't happen, you have failed. Think of your daily practice as something that is there for you to return to when you are ready. It might not actually be every day. And, it might not happen for a year or years. It is always there for you – waiting, ready, lovingly for you.

Consider, if you were to create a daily practice, what might it look like to really speak to you and motivate you. Identify what inspires you and what would ignite a beginning. In your asana practice, let your body guide you rather than follow a script. Get in touch with how you are feeling that day on your mat and let that feeling inspire the practice.

Nugget #2 – Keep a Journal

I have found that keeping a journal allows me to "remember" key insights, connections of those insights to my personal life and journey, references to other teacher's quotes, etc. In your journal, you might wish to jot down reflections from your home practice, take notes in class with another teacher, or write out your flows for class that you wish to practice and tweak.

When I teach a class, I bring my journal with me. I may not open it at all and, sometimes, based on who is in the class, the intention we have set and the feel of the room, I will open it up and pull the most precious reading to share. I write out my most favorite flows and, on the days where I am struggling to focus, will flip to those pages before class and review to set myself up for success in leading the class.

Remember, this is your journal. There is no "right way" or "wrong way" to set it up. I use a journal that allows me to remove, rearrange or transfer pages within the book or to another book with ease. I have a journal for my personal asana practice and for creating yoga sequences and routines I use in class and another that is mostly favorite readings that I have captured. If you are worried about other people reading your journal, buy one with a lock and key!

Nugget #3 – Create an Intention/Theme for the Class

When you prepare for teaching a class, remember, it is not about you! It is about your students. And how many times have you heard that? Plenty, I am sure. Though we know this – in practice, we may forget. And forgetting looks like – worrying about whether they are listening to you, worrying about "getting it right," worrying about how "good" you are doing, etc. What I know to be true is that the students in our classes want to grow and they want to be led to their growth. It is through our own humanity as teachers that allows the students' humanity to come forth. Trusting yourself is trusting others.

For each class, choose an intention/theme from something you are discovering for yourself or that is resonating as a community. It's not about making it up. Choose from a place of personal experience, shared humanity or what you are curious about. It doesn't have to be serious. In fact, encouraging inquiry as playful and fun relaxes and engages your students. I will generally pick an intention for the asana practice (i.e., hip opening, breath, standing poses, etc.) then weave a theme for inquiry into the teaching (i.e., focus on a Yama, Niyama, Sutra, incorrect belief, etc.). Share a personal example, or insight with the class then relate it to the overall theme, such as non-violence, to make it more universal, and bring it back to your students and the pose.

One of the types of yoga that I teach is restorative yoga. For each class I consider what the intention/theme will be, design the sequence and pull breath exercises, meditations and readings for each pose. My primary focus is to bring comfort to my students in this practice. We use props to allow the body to be comfortable and to allow for surrender in the pose. I will only speak at the beginning and allow for silence for at least eight minutes in each pose. My focus in the speaking is to offer a way to breath in the pose, to allow for an understanding of how the body is benefiting from the pose, and to share a reading that fits with the theme and allows for inquiry while resting.

In setting up for your class, you must always consider that you may have to throw out your plan completely based on what happens when you arrive. There have been times when I have taught restorative yoga when we did not have enough or the right props. There have been times in a vinyasa flow class that I have had beginner students and modified the flow to accommodate so that the beginners could flow with the more experienced students. And, there have been times when only one student shows up, and I craft the class as a private for them to address what they want to focus on. My point is, be prepared and be ready for anything!

Kathi Crawford is a 200 Hour Registered Yoga Teacher. When she is not on her mat, Kathi is guiding, coaching and inspiring others to realize and act upon their potential in the workplace. She is the Founder of People Possibilities, LLC whose mission is to change the culture of business one leader at a time.

More often than not, I can be seen wearing a delicate, silver chain with two small initial pendants, a lovely gift from one of my dear students. The initials aren't my name but instead signify a descriptive cue I often use in my teaching, which tickles her. That necklace is now like my talisman, a closely held reminder of the reach of my own voice.

It's natural when you first graduate to find yourself a bit paralyzed by the vision of Ideal Yoga Teacher. You've fallen head over heels in love with the practice. You've likely fallen in love with a teacher or teachers along the way. You want, desperately at times, to do right by all of it. You want what you're offering to be worthy, and, of course, there is the fear that it won't be, couldn't possibly be. You're too green, the training was too little, too fast, and everyone else is so knowledgeable. Frequently the beginning of teaching is a mix of emulation, trying to check off invisible "must do" boxes, and frankly, feeling like a fraud. The traditional advice offered to fix this is to teach from what you know. Just keep teaching from your practice. Things will sort themselves, and you'll find your own voice. This is true, but only to an extent, as oftentimes, the practices fallen back on were learned in training.

Truly, to find your voice and settle into it, however, is to first change that picture of Ideal Yoga Teacher. The picture that needs to come into focus is you as Yoga Teacher. Will that happen overnight? Not likely. But if the only vision in your mind is some lofty other as a goal, your teaching will always ring hollow and subsequently students will feel that disconnect.

Instead of overwhelming yourself with direct, designed to be helpful, clarifying questions like:

What do you want to teach?
What kind of teacher are you?
Where do you see yourself teaching?
Who is your ideal student?

which can invariably lead to stalling out with "I don't know," the protesting "yeah but," or fearful "nobody would come to that" answers, consider the following for a different approach:

Next time you find yourself gushing to others about yoga, what do you hear yourself say?
If you think about what keeps you coming back to your mat and practice, is there a pattern?
If you've taken extra classes and trainings, what have you really enjoyed?

Talk these things through with a trusted friend or mentor, write your findings down, and pay close attention to how you feel when you attend a class or workshop. Taking the time for this sort of inquiry can feel like time you don't have, but it's all a part of bringing the vision of you as Yoga Teacher into focus. The things you get excited about, the things that interest you, are the things that you will feel confident and comfortable in offering. Allowing it to come to you through a process of exploration can help to solidify it, to make it tangible, and sidestep that natural inclination to let doubt rule. Think about it in the way you would break down an asana in your training; you can read about it in a textbook, you can hear the instruction, but when you feel it in your own body, everything makes a different sort of sense.

A huge piece of this entire puzzle is then allowing yourself to be open to learning from your students. The people who show up in your room shape your voice and teachings by the nature of how we communicate with one another. Not every cue will land; you are not every student's teacher. It's both bigger and smaller than that. There is a particular description of the Sanskrit word for trust, Nyasa, that I feel is relevant here. Manorama says, "Trust is a gift you bestow on someone." A student coming to your classes is a gift of trust; they trust your offering, your voice. Your job is to bestow the gift of trust on yourself to allow your offering, your voice to come through. The rest will, as they say, sort itself.

Jessica Boyd is a 40-something wife, mother, dog-obsessed, lover of travel and oftentimes a curmudgeonly yoga teacher. Currently living in Houston, TX with roots in the desert of Arizona.

Dear teacher,

I must tell you this: there is no such thing as "perfect practice." There is practice, and there is the absence of practice. The single skill of a powerful teacher is that they practice. What you practice, and therefore what you teach, must be a reflection of the undulating needs and interests of your personal quest. When you are asked to deal with tragedy in your life, dive into your practice - what techniques and methods do you find to be healing? When you find yourself dealing with fatigue or injury, what aspects of the practice do you find antagonizing? Which aspects are comforting? What other techniques and healing modalities do you find supplemental? Share what you've learned with your students, because each challenge you confront along the way is your fuel, not your impediment.

After all the trainings, workshops, mentorships and master classes, what will make you a great teacher is your desire to investigate and share your own personal experience. The path of teaching extends only as far as the depth of your practice, which is dependent on your willingness to explore your limits, habits, and quirks. If you're willing to wake up to your insecurity, your confusion, your competitive streak, your rebel edge, you'll tap into the HEALING power of the practice, rather than the pastime or hobby of practice.

The next most important aspect of the path is that you have a teacher and a community to facilitate your growth and hold you accountable. There are so many things we could all be practicing, and at a certain point in your path, you will find yourself trying to take it all in. At first, this is useful. Try on the restorative and feel its effects. Try on the Ashtanga sequence and feel its effects. Take a yin training and learn about the fascia system. When you find yourself truly turned on by a particular tradition - when you feel yourself held and supported by teachings that go way beyond your fluctuating interests and trends - you will find a teacher to witness your progress and provide you with an anchor when you feel the (very human) urge to pull away and move on. It's a lot like monogamy in its challenges and rewards. It all comes down to commitment and reckoning with yourself in a container that is based on love and devotion.

What you practice, and perhaps even why, will change. The challenges and conundrums of being a human person in relationship to other human people are why we practice at all. Challenges and conundrums are the friction needed to ignite your spark. Remember, you are the primary resource on your path. Your particularities, combined with the teachings, tossed together in the soup of real life are the gold. Keep a healthy perspective on it - while we talk about "The Path," it's your path. You will see the trees differently than I have, you will notice what is useful to you. Your teacher will guide your eyes to elements of the path you may not have noticed on your own, but ultimately you decide where to focus. When you have that sense of direction, you will be stronger in your resolve to navigate the obstacles, and you will become invaluable to your students. We're all in this together.

Stacey Ramsower is a Doula, seeker, lover, teacher, healing the world one body at a time. www.staceymoves.com

"Be suspicious of what you want."

- Rumi

Part 7:

Your Offering

Your Offering

You are unique. No one in the whole world can offer a yoga class precisely as you can. Helping you know what differentiates you from others will allow you to add to your confidence level, and you will be less likely to compare yourself to others. In the above chapters, you have clarified who you know yourself to be, and what you desire to grow into. You have something to share that adds value to others.

Recognize the value of what you are delivering.

What value do you know for sure you have given by being a yoga teacher? Write it down.

Acknowledging it in your head is great but not half as powerful as writing it down by hand on paper.

How have you helped your students? It could be off the mat as well as on the mat. Don't say you don't know -- you won't know all the ways, but you will know many of the ways. Maybe you listened to a student after class who needed a friend, you made a new student feel welcome, or you created a safe space so that a student could be in child's pose for most of the class without any pressure to perform.

What makes you unique as a yoga teacher, a human being?

What is the conversation you wish to have with others and yourself?

Who is the audience that you want to reach?

Who do you attract to your classes?

You have something to share that adds value to others. Recognize the value of what you are delivering. Keep it simple and clear.

Understanding How You're Perceived

Perceptions are funny things. We think we are transparent and that people see us the way we see ourselves, but that isn't necessarily so. More often than not it is far from the truth. I bought a used "fancier" type of car with funds my mother left me after her death. I had many reasons for making the purchase. My twelve-year-old VW was on its last legs, I had always wanted a luxury item, and I thought my mom would be happy that I had bought myself something fancy; however, the main reason was this. A few months prior a drunk driver had fallen asleep at the wheel and driven his car into my house; one person died, one was severely wounded. Security and feeling safe became a higher priority for me.

My new car gave me this sensation. It was interesting how several people made comments about how well my yoga business must be doing, based solely on the car I now drove. Our yoga business was the same as it had been. Nothing had changed with yoga, I had a death in the family and an accident at home. So much of what is perceived about us *has nothing to do with us*, it's projections and labels that other people put onto us. I mention it here, not for you to change any of your behavior, or likes, or teachings but for the awareness that you can use other's perceptions of you as a gauge when needed.

How you are perceived will attract a particular student to your class, If you want a different audience you can change this perception. You have the power. If you don't know, ask. I do this exercise whenever I feel I've lost track; I ask a friend of mine or yoga colleague, which often are the same, to answer the following questions. This inquiry does not have to be limited to your "yoga world," perceptions show up in all areas of our lives. You can use this at home, at work, in family dynamics. Make sure the partner you ask for help understands the exercise and its value to you. This is not a "tell-me-how-fabulous-I-am" ego boost.

1. *What do you most appreciate about me?*
2. *What do you see that I could continue doing that supports my authenticity?*
3. *When do you see me give away my power?*
4. *If you didn't know me what "story" would you make up about me?*
5. *What perception did you have of me when you first met me?*

Success

Our perceptions of success are as individualistic and varied as how we choose to teach a class. If you have a high value on finances, you will most likely define success as how much you earn as a teacher. If you have a high value on the physical you probably will define success has how healthy or flexible, or strong your students are becoming. If you are inspired by spirituality and meditation success might be how much your students love your guidance, your knowledge of spiritual teachings and various religions. If you want your students to have fun more than anything else that will be your rubric for gauging your success.

How do you currently define success for yourself as a yoga teacher?

In what areas are you successful already?

In what areas would you like to see your success grow?

What are you willing to do to make that happen?

Supplemental Information

Video Assessment

One of the best and fastest ways you can learn about your "delivery skill set" as a yoga teacher is through viewing and hearing yourself "live." Record yourself teaching a class with video and audio. If you are uncomfortable filming yourself in front of a class of students- teach a class to an empty room but don't cheat yourself- teach the whole class as if it was full of your students. Watch 3 minutes of your video and answer the following. Then watch the next 3 or 5 minutes and then the next. It's one thing for someone to give you feedback, it's another one completely to see yourself "live." It will be uncomfortable and affirming. This exercise can be transformative, let yourself be transformed!

Your View

What are three strengths that you demonstrated in your teaching?

What are three things that you had not realized need work immediately?

What are three things that you would like to improve in the near future?

Ask a friend, whose opinion your trust, to watch a few minutes of your video and give you feedback. What did she/ he notice? (Refer to the following pages on how to give and receive feedback appropriately.)

What are 3 action steps that you are willing to commit to today? Make sure they are simple and clear so that you will know when you have completed them. Set a "by when" date. Unless there is a "by when" finish date for actions we find challenging, we won't do them.

Feedback

Feedback is constructive observations and evaluation to improve your teaching skills. Any teacher that is truly interested in growth seeks it out. Whether *asked or unasked* it is an important element to becoming a more compelling teacher. Knowing how to give feedback will help you communicate with your colleagues and students also.

This feedback is not to question your ability to teach; it is already understood that you are passionate about teaching and want to be more effective. This is about delivery, self-perception and how you are perceived by others.

Why is it important?

Self-perception can be blind to both our "positive" and "negative" side. We create habits and without realizing it set up frameworks that might have served us well in the past but don't serve us anymore. We get "stuck" and don't see where we might be stale; we repeat things, become tuned out to the experience we are giving. We can start to believe "stories" about our selves that are not true. Choose well when you select someone to give you feedback. Feedback is useless and can be harmful if coming from someone who does not understand your intention for teaching or doesn't have your best interest at heart.

Benefits of receiving it:
- See our strengths
- See our blind spots
- Find areas of potential growth
- Remain a student, aware we are not "done."
- Gives you the opportunity to see what is important to you as a teacher.
- i.e., if you get feedback that your class would be better with music and you prefer no music in class, you have the opportunity to recommit to your truth. What feels "right" to you? Stick with that.

How to receive feedback

Feedback is meant to help you become more empowered, confident and aware. It helps you change, but you don't have to change anything if you choose not to. If you consistently get the same feedback, the question then becomes why are you attached to doing something a certain way? How does your way of doing something serve you and your students?

- Come from a place of humility and gratitude.
- Know the feedback is given here from a place of love.
- Be willing to hear what is being said, listen well.
- Notice if you feel defensive, if you want to interrupt- this is normal.
- Do not interrupt.
- Acknowledge the feedback- say thank you.

NOTE: Do not give your "personal power" away. Just because a person you trust says something about your teaching doesn't mean that her truth needs to become your truth. To continue with the example above about music, your "feedback person" might have a very strong opinion that yoga class is always better with music. You might not feel the same way. If you are not sure, "sit with" the feedback for a day or two and check back in with your higher "Self." If it doesn't feel right, say "thank you" and drop it.

You never need to apologize for the kind of class you teach. Everyone will have an opinion. Again, be selective in who you choose, don't take your feedback remarks in and try to make them fit if they don't.

Also, note that we often unconsciously choose to only hear the "negative" feedback and drop into a negative spiral. Don't do that! Give yourself permission to celebrate all you are doing really well, hear the "positives" and celebrate those qualities. Our lower "self" wants to keep us small, let your higher "Self" win out.

After receiving feedback, you can:

Consider what you heard and absorb the information
Check-in: Does it "ring true"? Is there any truth to what was said? If it doesn't fit drop the information, let it go.

Giving Feedback

Before your colleague, friend, or mentor watches your video (or observes your class) go over the following list below with them. Remind them to:

Be specific
Comment on the action, not the person
You are here to improve the quality of the experience
Make sure the feedback is helpful, making someone wrong is not what you are here to do.
e.g. "When you said, 'connect to your bandhas,' I didn't know what you meant."

What did you as a "viewer"/ "student" experience? Speak to the following qualities:

- Language
  - Was the language clear and purposeful or confusing?
  - Were there "filler" words? Repetitive words? (i.e. "and then," "um," "beautiful")
  - Word choices (that foot vs. your foot)
  - Other...

- Tempo/Rhythm of the class
  - Too fast, too slow, connected with breath, steady...
  - Other...
- Body Language/Posture (look at feet, hands, eye contact, head)
  - Was it assertive? (hands on hips)
  - Was it meek? (head down)
  - Was it confident?
  - Was it restless? (too much movement)
  - Was it heavy? (staying in one place)
  - Was it nervous? (pacing, unsettled, floaty)
  - Other...
- Voice
  - How was the quality of the voice? Was it energetic, did it have presence?
  - Was it "sing-songy yoga teacher voice" or monotone?)
  - Was it weak, not audible?
  - Where was the voice coming from? Throat or core? (The voice will feel more rooted and grounded if coming from your core)
  - Other...
- Authenticity
  - Did you "feel" her/him? (her presence, energy, delight, message, intention)
  - Did you feel "connected" to the teacher? And the teacher connected with you the student?
  - Did the teacher resonate with the content of her teaching? Or was it just "yoga speak"?
- Intention
  - What was the overall outcome of taking this teacher's "class"?
  - Did the teacher interfere with your experience of the practice?
  - Did your teacher enhance your experience of the practice?
  - Did the teacher "hold space" for her students?
  - Was the teacher mindful in thought, word, and action?
- What worked powerfully? Describe elements that were great.
- What could be added to make it an even better experience?
- What could be shed?

This is a long checklist, do not get discouraged! Many of the above areas you do well already, there are probably only a few that could use some improvement. If you can tell after watching your own recording what needs work- revise and then a week, or a month later, record yourself again. Ask for several people to give you feedback. Remember yoga is a practice, teaching yoga is a practice. We don't arrive and say "I have Mastered Teaching!" You can be a masterful teacher and still not have mastered teaching. We are all works in progress.

B. K. S. Iyengar has a beautiful paragraph in his book "The Tree of Yoga." He speaks about being a beginner in yoga and how each day he wants to be a beginner because he wants new experiences. He's not looking for what he's already done, that is old news- he wants to see what is new that he can learn today. We are all beginners; we are also yogis with hundreds or thousands of hours on our mats.

Review (Pre-teaching)

Before teaching a class, review and answer the following:

The theme for class: Mental (quieting the mind), Physical (anatomy), Emotional (well-being), Devotional (speaking to spirit), Historical (yoga sutras, lineage of yoga...)

- What is your intention with the words you choose for this class?
- What is your intention for your choice of poses for this class?
- What is your intention for how you will teach the class?
- (i.e., will you demo poses often and go slowly since there are many new students?)
- If you will physically assist your students in class, what is the intention behind your touch?

Review (Post-teaching)

Review how the class went. What was the feedback you received (visually, verbally, energetically, etc.)?

- What would you keep?
- What would you change?
- Was this class about you or them? Was the feedback from your students about you or them?

Reminders

- Honor Yourself. You are the expert on you.

- Have a plan. AND be willing to drop the plan when it's not working.

- Don't compare yourself to others doing the same thing. Comparison is toxic.

- Speak from your own experience, not from what you have been told. *Your own story is powerful.*

- It's okay to not know. Being able to say "I don't know" is much more powerful than pretending to know.

- You will inspire and you will disappoint. Get over both and get on with it.

- Accentuate the positive. Show up. Be present.

- Develop your observations skills. Use them. Most communication is non-verbal.

- Consistency is powerful. Find a rhythm for you and how you teach your classes.

- Authenticity is energizing, economical and efficient. (You will never be in your power if you are trying to be someone you are not.)

- Pay attention to what attracts you. Listen well. Do more of that (whatever it may be).

- You are here to share something unique. Share it.

- Who you are matters more than what you know.

- Be curious.

- Go ahead and be the person you wish to be now.

- Enjoy the journey.

Books that Inspire, Teach and Ground

Marianne Williamson, *A Return to Love*, 1996
Danielle LaPorte, *The Desire Map*, 2014 and "The White Hot Truth" 2017
Brené Brown, *Daring Greatly,* 2012
Bhagavad Gita, translation by Stephen Mitchell, 2000
Donna Farhi, *Bringing Yoga To Life*, 2004
Steve Ross, *Happy Yoga*, 2003
B.K.S. Iyengar, *The Tree of Yoga*, 1988

Earlier in this guide I mentioned that we never know why students come back to their mat unless they tell us. The list below is from female High School students that were taking yoga for the first time for PE credit. Their yoga teacher shared this with me a few years ago. I shared it with my students and am passing it along to you demonstrating again the power of what we practice and teach.

The prompt from their teacher:
I practice yoga because...

...I want to take my mind off of bad stuff.
...it helps me go through my dad with peace and calm.
...it helps me relax my mind from any negative thoughts floating around.
...we become a community and stick together.
...it helps me feel good about myself.
...it brings peace to my body.
...it changes how you see things around you.
...it is a good workout and I want a big butt.
...it helps me understand that I can do more than I think. It helps me realize my strength.
...it's a technique that I can use to connect with myself.
...I want to take care of my body.
...I get to challenge myself.
...I get to try new things.
...I love the feeling I get of becoming stronger.
...when you are done, you feel light, like nothing disturbs you anymore.
...I can be in my own little world.

Thank you.

A big thank you to my fellow yogis Jessica Boyd, Kathi Crawford, Elaine Eichelberger, Lindsay Parmer, Stacey Ramsower and Sarah Strom for saying yes and sharing their wisdom. A big thank you and shout-out to Ret Paccasassi for her encouragement and help with the original manual and her support of this book. And a big thank you and hug to Elizabeth Haberer for saying yes to a "big ask" and doing so with grace and beauty. To all the yoga teachers that continue to share this practice and to all the students that practice, Thank you.

About the Author

Maria Merrill was introduced to yoga in 1999 and has been teaching since 2003. She believes in the power of yoga and the immeasurable gifts the practice can give. One of her favorite things is to share what brings her joy. She loves to teach, mentor, and write. She lives in Houston, Texas. You can find her at www.maria-merrill.com.

Made in the
USA
Monee, IL